小時代
Chinese School
A Little Dynasty
中文學校
ORGANIC

Welcome to the magical world of Go Boo Boo where learning Chinese is FUN!

Your children will be singing and laughing their way to Mandarin Chinese fluency in no time at all with Boo Boo and his friends.

Boo Boo's Chinese Grooves for Kids Volume 1

Songs and Sing Along Book Published by A Little Dynasty Productions, LLC
9844 Research Drive, Irvine, California 92618
United States of America
www.gobooboo.com www.alittledynasty.com
Songs written by A. Liu and C. Liu, artwork by C. Liu

ISBN: 978-1-939208-00-2

Printed in Taiwan, ROC

CD Tracks Song • Karaoke		Lyrics Page
1 • 13	A Little Dynasty 小時代	2
2 • 14	Ni Hao My Friend 你好我的朋友	4
3 • 15	Shape World 形狀世界	6
4 • 16	My Name is Boo Boo 我叫做 Boo Boo	8
5 • 17	123 Freeze 一二三木頭人	10
6 • 18	Dragon Boat 划龍舟	12
7 • 19	Ten Little Friends 十個小朋友	14
8 • 20	Manners Song 禮貌歌	16
9 • 21	Owie Aiya Song 不小心就受傷	18
10 • 22	Where's Boo Boo? Boo Boo 在哪裡？	20
11 • 23	Night Market 逛夜市	22
12 • 24	Goodbye My Friend 再見我的朋友	24

1
A Little Dynasty
小時代
小時代
Chinese School
A Little Dynasty
中文學校

A Little Dynasty · 小時代 Xiǎo Shí Dài

小時代真好玩我們一起學中文
xiǎo shí dài zhēn hǎo wán wǒ men yì qǐ xué zhōng wén
A Little Dynasty is Really Fun, Let's Learn Chinese Together!

每一天有禮貌身體健康精神好
měi yì tiān yǒu lǐ mào shēn tǐ jiàn kāng jīng shén hǎo
Every Day, be Polite, Healthy, and Energetic!

一二三四五六七紅橙黃綠藍靛紫
yī èr sān sì wǔ liù qī hóng chéng huáng lǜ lán diàn zǐ
1234567 Red, Orange, Yellow, Green, Blue, Violet, Purple

小時代學中文唱歌跳舞真快樂
xiǎo shí dài xué zhōng wén chàng gē tiào wǔ zhēn kuài lè
Learning Chinese, Singing and Dancing is Fun at A Little Dynasty!

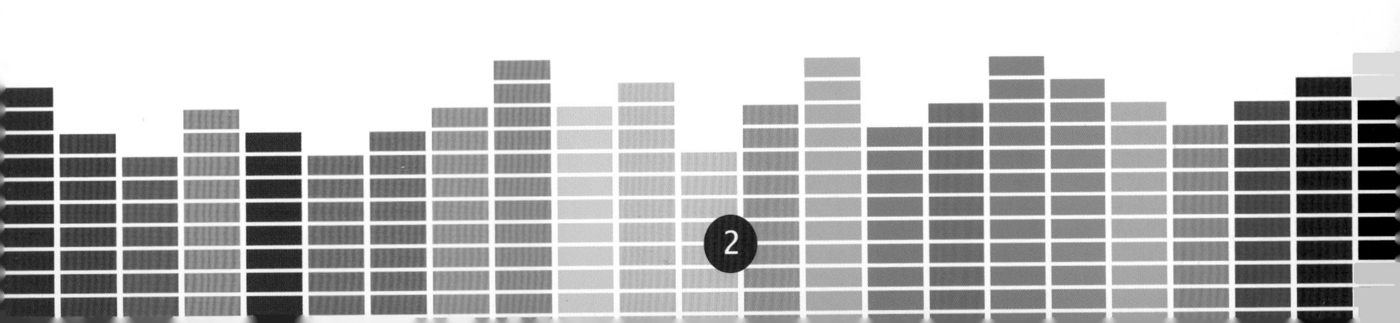

2
Nǐ Hǎo My Friend
你好我的朋友

Nǐ Hǎo My Friend · 你好我的朋友

ㄋㄧˇ ㄏㄠˇ ㄨㄛˇ ˙ㄉㄜ ㄆㄥˊ ㄧㄡˇ
Nǐ Hǎo Wǒ De Péng Yǒu

每天見面時候說你好
ㄇㄟˇ ㄊㄧㄢ ㄐㄧㄢˋ ㄇㄧㄢˋ ㄕˊ ㄏㄡˋ ㄕㄨㄛ ㄋㄧˇ ㄏㄠˇ
měi tiān jiàn miàn shí hòu shuō nǐ hǎo
Say Hello Every Day When Meeting

每天上學時候說你好
ㄇㄟˇ ㄊㄧㄢ ㄕㄤˋ ㄒㄩㄝˊ ㄕˊ ㄏㄡˋ ㄕㄨㄛ ㄋㄧˇ ㄏㄠˇ
měi tiān shàng xué shí hòu shuō nǐ hǎo
Say Hello Every Day at School

看見老師說你好看見朋友說你好
ㄎㄢˋ ㄐㄧㄢˋ ㄌㄠˇ ㄕ ㄕㄨㄛ ㄋㄧˇ ㄏㄠˇ ㄎㄢˋ ㄐㄧㄢˋ ㄆㄥˊ ㄧㄡˇ ㄕㄨㄛ ㄋㄧˇ ㄏㄠˇ
kàn jiàn lǎo shī shuō nǐ hǎo kàn jiàn péng yǒu shuō nǐ hǎo
Say Hello When You See Your Teacher and Your Friends

說你好大家都笑說你好要有禮貌
ㄕㄨㄛ ㄋㄧˇ ㄏㄠˇ ㄉㄚˋ ㄐㄧㄚ ㄉㄡ ㄒㄧㄠˋ ㄕㄨㄛ ㄋㄧˇ ㄏㄠˇ ㄧㄠˋ ㄧㄡˇ ㄌㄧˇ ㄇㄠˋ
shuō nǐ hǎo dà jiā dōu xiào shuō nǐ hǎo yào yǒu lǐ mào
Saying Hello Makes Everyone Smile and is Polite

我的朋友你好你好我好大家好
ㄨㄛˇ ˙ㄉㄜ ㄆㄥˊ ㄧㄡˇ ㄋㄧˇ ㄏㄠˇ ㄋㄧˇ ㄏㄠˇ ㄨㄛˇ ㄏㄠˇ ㄉㄚˋ ㄐㄧㄚ ㄏㄠˇ
wǒ de péng yǒu nǐ hǎo nǐ hǎo wǒ hǎo dà jiā hǎo
Hello My Friend, I'm Well, Hello Everyone

我的朋友你好我們一起說你好
ㄨㄛˇ ˙ㄉㄜ ㄆㄥˊ ㄧㄡˇ ㄋㄧˇ ㄏㄠˇ ㄨㄛˇ ˙ㄇㄣ ㄧˋ ㄑㄧˇ ㄕㄨㄛ ㄋㄧˇ ㄏㄠˇ
wǒ de péng yǒu nǐ hǎo wǒ men yì qǐ shuō nǐ hǎo
Hello My Friend, Let's Say Hello Together

3
Shape World
形狀世界

Shape World · 形狀世界

Xíng Zhuàng Shì Jiè

圓形的球在地上拍

yuán xíng de qiú zài dì shàng pāi

Pat a Round Shaped Ball on the Ground

三角形的積木疊的高高的

sān jiǎo xíng de jī mù dié de gāo gāo de

Stack Triangle Shaped Blocks so High

正方形的桌子它有四個腳

zhèng fāng xíng de zhuō zi tā yǒu sì ge jiǎo

The Square Shaped Table Has Four Legs

形狀世界真好玩

xíng zhuàng shì jiè zhēn hǎo wán

Shape World is Really Fun

4

My Name is Boo Boo
我叫做 Boo Boo

My Name is Boo Boo・我叫做 Boo Boo

ㄨㄛˇ ㄐㄧㄠˋ ㄗㄨㄛˋ
Wǒ Jiào Zuò

我叫做 Boo Boo 我喜歡跳舞
ㄨㄛˇ ㄐㄧㄠˋ ㄗㄨㄛˋ ㄨㄛˇ ㄒㄧˇ ㄏㄨㄢ ㄊㄧㄠˋ ㄨˇ
wǒ jiào zuò wǒ xǐ huān tiào wǔ

My Name is Boo Boo, I Like to Dance

跟我跳 Boo Boo 舞
ㄍㄣ ㄨㄛˇ ㄊㄧㄠˋ ㄨˇ
gēn wǒ tiào wǔ

Let's Do the Boo Boo Dance

游泳打蒼蠅
ㄧㄡˊ ㄩㄥˇ ㄉㄚˇ ㄘㄤ ㄧㄥˊ
yóu yǒng dǎ cāng yíng

Swimming, Fly Swatting

挖土吃草肚子痛
ㄨㄚ ㄊㄨˇ ㄔ ㄘㄠˇ ㄉㄨˋ ㄗ ㄊㄨㄥˋ
wā tǔ chī cǎo dù zi tòng

Digging, Grazing, Stomach Ache

就跳到這裡
ㄐㄧㄡˋ ㄊㄧㄠˋ ㄉㄠˋ ㄓㄜˋ ㄌㄧˇ
jiù tiào dào zhè lǐ

The Dance Ends Here

5

123 Freeze
一二三木頭人

123 Freeze・一二三木頭人 Yī Èr Sān Mù Tóu Rén

一 二 三 木 頭 人 我 們 一 起 來 比 賽
yī èr sān mù tóu rén wǒ men yì qǐ lái bǐ sài
One, Two, Three, Freeze (Turn to Wood), Let's Complete

一 二 三 木 頭 人 看 誰 最 先 到 終 點
yī èr sān mù tóu rén kàn shéi zuì xiān dào zhōng diǎn
One, Two, Three, Freeze (Turn to Wood), Who Will Finish First

一 二 一 二 一 二 三 走 走 停 停 真 好 玩
yī èr yī èr yī èr sān zǒu zǒu tíng tíng zhēn hǎo wán
One, Two, One, Two, One, Two, Three, Going and Stopping is so Fun

一 二 三 木 頭 人 我 們 都 是 第 一 名
yī èr sān mù tóu rén wǒ men dōu shì dì yī míng
One, Two, Three, Freeze (Turn to Wood), We're All In First Place

6
Dragon Boat
划龍舟

Dragon Boat · 划ㄏㄨㄚˊ 龍ㄌㄨㄥˊ 舟ㄓㄡ
Huá Lóng Zhōu

划ㄏㄨㄚˊ 龍ㄌㄨㄥˊ 舟ㄓㄡ 划ㄏㄨㄚˊ 龍ㄌㄨㄥˊ 舟ㄓㄡ
huá lóng zhōu huá lóng zhōu

Row the Dragon Boat, Row the Dragon Boat

端ㄉㄨㄢ 午ㄨˇ 節ㄐㄧㄝˊ 要ㄧㄠˋ 划ㄏㄨㄚˊ 龍ㄌㄨㄥˊ 舟ㄓㄡ
duān wǔ jié yào huá lóng zhōu

Row the Dragon Boat on the Moon Festival

嘿ㄏㄟ 喲ㄧㄠ 嘿ㄏㄟ 喲ㄧㄠ 嘿ㄏㄟ 嘿ㄏㄟ 喲ㄧㄠ
hēi yāo hēi yāo hēi hēi yāo

Hei-Yo, Hei-Yo, Hei-Hei Yo

大ㄉㄚˋ 家ㄐㄧㄚ 一ㄧˋ 起ㄑㄧˇ 喊ㄏㄢˇ 加ㄐㄧㄚ 油ㄧㄡˊ
dà jiā yì qǐ hǎn jiā yóu

Let's All Cheer Together

看ㄎㄢˋ 誰ㄕㄟˊ 最ㄗㄨㄟˋ 先ㄒㄧㄢ 到ㄉㄠˋ 終ㄓㄨㄥ 點ㄉㄧㄢˇ
kàn shéi zuì xiān dào zhōng diǎn

See Who Finishes First

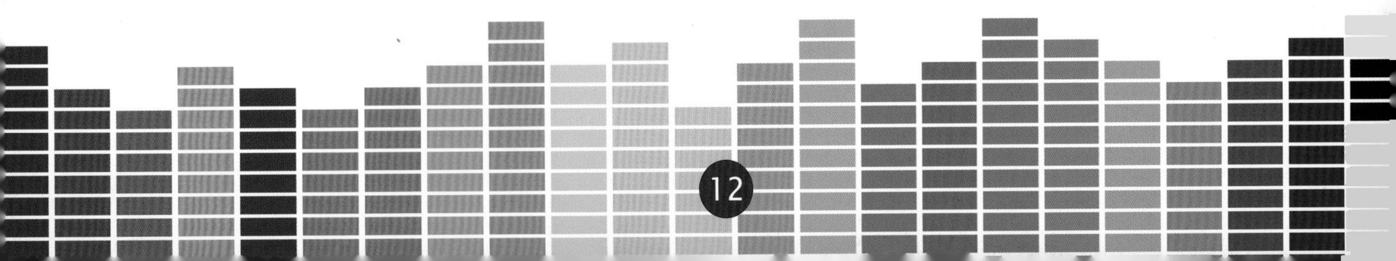

7
Ten Little Friends
十個小朋友
1
2
3
4
5
6
7
8
9
10

Ten Little Friends · 十(ㄕˊ) 個(˙ㄍㄜ) 小(ㄒㄧㄠˇ) 朋(ㄆㄥˊ) 友(ㄧㄡˇ)

Shí Ge Xiǎo Péng Yǒu

有(ㄧㄡˇ) 一(ㄧˊ) 個(˙ㄍㄜ) 有(ㄧㄡˇ) 兩(ㄌㄧㄤˇ) 個(˙ㄍㄜ) 有(ㄧㄡˇ) 三(ㄙㄢ) 個(˙ㄍㄜ) 小(ㄒㄧㄠˇ) 朋(ㄆㄥˊ) 友(ㄧㄡˇ)

yǒu yí ge yǒu liǎng ge yǒu sān ge xiǎo péng yǒu

There is One, There are Two, There are Three Little Friends

有(ㄧㄡˇ) 四(ㄙˋ) 個(˙ㄍㄜ) 有(ㄧㄡˇ) 五(ㄨˇ) 個(˙ㄍㄜ) 有(ㄧㄡˇ) 六(ㄌㄧㄡˋ) 個(˙ㄍㄜ) 小(ㄒㄧㄠˇ) 朋(ㄆㄥˊ) 友(ㄧㄡˇ)

yǒu sì ge yǒu wǔ ge yǒu liù ge xiǎo péng yǒu

There are Four, There are Five, There are Six Little Friends

有(ㄧㄡˇ) 七(ㄑㄧ) 個(˙ㄍㄜ) 有(ㄧㄡˇ) 八(ㄅㄚ) 個(˙ㄍㄜ) 有(ㄧㄡˇ) 九(ㄐㄧㄡˇ) 個(˙ㄍㄜ) 小(ㄒㄧㄠˇ) 朋(ㄆㄥˊ) 友(ㄧㄡˇ)

yǒu qī ge yǒu bā ge yǒu jiǔ ge xiǎo péng yǒu

There are Seven, There are Eight, There are Nine Little Friends

有(ㄧㄡˇ) 十(ㄕˊ) 個(˙ㄍㄜ) 小(ㄒㄧㄠˇ) 朋(ㄆㄥˊ) 友(ㄧㄡˇ)

yǒu shí ge xiǎo péng yǒu

There are Ten Little Friends

8 Manners Song 禮貌歌

Manners Song · 禮貌歌

Lǐ Mào Gē

大家要分享不要搶東西

dà jiā yào fēn xiǎng bú yào qiǎng dōng xī

Everyone Should Share, Don't Grab Things

請謝謝對不起要常常對人說

qǐng xiè xie duì bù qǐ yào cháng cháng duì rén shuō

Say "Please" "Thank You" and "Sorry" Often

對人有禮貌見人笑嘻嘻

duì rén yǒu lǐ mào jiàn rén xiào xī xī

Be Polite and Smile When You Meet Someone

不推人不爭吵做個好小孩

bù tuī rén bù zhēng chǎo zuò ge hǎo xiǎo hái

Don't Push, Don't Quarrel, Be a Good Kid

9 Owie Aiya Song
不小心就受傷

Owie Ai Ya Song · 不小心就受傷

Bù Xiǎo Xīn Jiù Shòu Shāng

如果玩具你沒收好你就容易摔跤

rú guǒ wán jù nǐ méi shōu hǎo nǐ jiù róng yì shuāi jiāo

If You Don't Put Your Toys Away You Can Easily Get Hurt

ㄠ - ㄠ - 好痛啊!

hǎo tòng a

Ow, Ow, It Really Hurts!

不小心就受傷

bù xiǎo xīn jiù shòu shāng

If You are Not Careful, You Will Get Hurt

如果手拿鉛筆亂跑你就容易受傷

rú guǒ shǒu ná qiān bǐ luàn pǎo nǐ jiù róng yì shòu shāng

If You Run Around With a Pencil You Can Easily Get Hurt

哎呀好痛啊!

āi ya hǎo tòng a

Ai Ya, It Really Hurts!

不小心就受傷

bù xiǎo xīn jiù shòu shāng

If You Are Not Careful, You Will Get Hurt

10
Where's Boo Boo?
Boo Boo 在哪裡？

Where's Boo Boo? · Boo Boo 在哪裡？

ㄗㄞˋ ㄋㄚˇ ㄌㄧˇ

Zài Nǎ Lǐ

Boo Boo 在ㄗㄞˋ 哪ㄋㄚˇ 裡ㄌㄧˇ Boo Boo 在ㄗㄞˋ 哪ㄋㄚˇ 裡ㄌㄧˇ

zài nǎ lǐ zài nǎ lǐ

Where is Boo Boo, Where is Boo Boo

我ㄨㄛˇ 們˙ㄇㄣ 一ㄧˋ 起ㄑㄧˇ 找ㄓㄠˇ 看ㄎㄢˋ 他ㄊㄚ 在ㄗㄞˋ 哪ㄋㄚˇ 裡ㄌㄧˇ

wǒ men yì qǐ zhǎo kàn tā zài nǎ lǐ

Let's Look for Him Together

這ㄓㄜˋ 邊ㄅㄧㄢ 找ㄓㄠˇ 一ㄧˋ 找ㄓㄠˇ 那ㄋㄚˋ 邊ㄅㄧㄢ 找ㄓㄠˇ 一ㄧˋ 找ㄓㄠˇ

zhè biān zhǎo yì zhǎo nà biān zhǎo yì zhǎo

Look Around Here, Look Around There

原ㄩㄢˊ 來ㄌㄞˊ Boo Boo 他ㄊㄚ 躲ㄉㄨㄛˇ 在ㄗㄞˋ 廁ㄘㄜˋ 所ㄙㄨㄛˇ 裡ㄌㄧˇ

yuán lái tā duǒ zài cè suǒ lǐ

Turns Out Boo Boo is Hiding in the Bathroom

原ㄩㄢˊ 來ㄌㄞˊ Boo Boo 他ㄊㄚ 已ㄧˇ 經ㄐㄧㄥ 睡ㄕㄨㄟˋ 著ㄓㄠˊ 了˙ㄌㄜ

yuán lái tā yǐ jīng shuì zháo le

Turns Out Boo Boo is Already Asleep

11
Night Market
逛夜市
菜市場
冰果店
雜
臭豆腐

Night Market · 逛夜市 Guàng Yè Shì

逛夜市逛夜市
guàng yè shì guàng yè shì

Shopping at the Night Market, Shopping at the Night Market

我們一起逛夜市
wǒ men yì qǐ guàng yè shì

Let's go Shopping Together at the Night Market

哥哥姐姐妹妹弟弟一起去
gē ge jiě jie mèi mei dì di yì qǐ qù

Big Brother, Big Sister, Little Sister, Little Brother, Let's All Go Together

我們一起逛夜市
wǒ men yì qǐ guàng yè shì

Let's go Shopping Together at the Night Market

12
Goodbye My Friend
再見我的朋友

Goodbye My Friend · 再見我的朋友
Zài Jiàn Wǒ De Péng Yǒu

揮一揮手再見我的朋友
huī yì huī shǒu zài jiàn wǒ de péng yǒu
Waving to You, Goodbye My Friend

今天我們快快樂樂的上學
jīn tiān wǒ men kuài kuài lè lè de shàng xué
We were Happy at School Today

親愛的好朋友
qīn ài de hǎo péng yǒu
My Dear Friend

捨不得和你說再見
shě bù dé hé nǐ shuō zài jiàn
I'm Reluctant to Say Goodbye to You

等待下次見面
děng dài xià cì jiàn miàn
I'll See You Next Time

開開心心說再見
kāi kāi xīn xīn shuō zài jiàn
So I'll Say Goodbye Happily